WELCOME

This annual belongs to:

....

MINI MYSTERY

There are **10** hidden fingerprints in this Annual that could be vital clues. Help the gang find them and list the page numbers below!

Answers on page 61.

4

Contents

WELL, IT'S GETTING LATE AND WE'VE GOT A BIG DAY TOMORROW.

WE'VE GOT A REENACTMENT AND AT THIS TIME OF YEAR IT SHOULD BE A BIG CROWD...IF THEY'RE NOT ALL SCARED OFF BY THE VIKINGS AGAIN!

DON'T YOU WORRY, NORMAN. WE'LL FIGURE THIS OUT.

SCOOB, IS THAT, LIKE, YOUR TUMMY MAKING THAT NOISE?

REAH! RI'M RUNGRY!

RUMBLE! BURBLE!

LIKE, ME TOO, LET'S GO FIND SOMETHING TO EAT!

RAHOO!

SSSHH! DON'T WAKE FREDDY!

LIKE, I HOPE THERE ARE SOME LEFTOVERS IN THE MYSTERY MACHINE.

RAGGY! ROOK!

YIKES! IT'S THE GHOST VIKINGS!

RHO-O-O-O-OSTS!

AND THEY SEE US!

LIKE, I NEVER THOUGHT I'D SAY THIS, BUT I'M MISSING THAT COZY NORMAN SETTLEMENT!

REAH!

PHEW! LIKE, THAT WAS TOO CLOSE FOR COMFORT!

SO, SCOOB, HOW DO WE GET DOWN FROM HERE?

DAPHNE! VELMA! IT'S SHAGGY AND SCOOBY -- THEY'VE DISAPPEARED!

THEY'RE PROBABLY JUST OUT LOOKING FOR A MIDNIGHT SNACK.

VIKINGS! OUT BEYOND THE WOODS! WE SAW THEM!

SO THEY DO EXIST!

THERE'S NOTHING WE CAN DO NOW, BUT I'VE GOT A PLAN FOR THE MORNING...

CONTINUED ON PAGE 14

A KNIGHT TO REMEMBER

THE GANG HAVE UNCOVERED SOME CROOKS FORGING FAMOUS PAINTINGS IN THE BASEMENT OF THE CITY MUSEUM. DISGUISED AS BLACK KNIGHTS THEY HAVE BEEN SCARING AWAY ANY SUSPICIOUS VISITORS! UNTIL NOW, THAT IS...

MUSEUM

Paul Gamble

CAN YOU FIND?

7 BLACK KNIGHTS
A BLACK CAT
AN OWL
2 BIPLANES
A SPACE SHUTTLE
AN EGYPTIAN MUMMY
THE MYSTERY MACHINE
A VINTAGE CAR
A TASTY DINO BONE
4 MATCHING PAINTINGS

13

AND THEN THE MARAUDING VIKING GHOSTS ATTACKED! THEY WERE SPECTRAL FORMS, DEATHLY PALE WITH BLOOD AND GORE STAINING THEIR WEAPONS...

...THE THRONGING MULTITUDE OF SPECTATORS SCREAMED AND TOOK TO THEIR HEELS IN PANIC!

L-LIKE, THAT'S A LOT OF VIKING GHOSTS!

COME ON, GUYS! WE'VE GOT TO TRY TO DO SOMETHING!

DRY ICE! AND SOME OF THESE CONTAINERS ARE ALREADY EMPTY.

SOMEONE AROUND HERE IS TRYING TO CREATE A SMOKESCREEN!

THE VIKING HORDES SENT THE NORMANS AND SAXONS SCATTERING IN ALL DIRECTIONS. AS THE CROWDS RAN IN FEAR...

...THE SPECTRAL HOST LEFT THE FIELD VICTORIOUS!

BOY, HAVE I GOT A SURPRISE FOR NORMAN!

IT'S THEM! IT'S THE VIKING GHOSTS!

YEAH, AND THERE'S A LOT OF THEM! LIKE, WHY EXACTLY ARE WE HERE AGAIN, VELMA?

RAGGY'S RIGHT! RET'S RET ROUTTA RERE!

SHHH! JUST WAIT... AND WATCH!

THEY'RE PEOPLE DRESSED UP AS GHOSTS!

YEAH, BUT, LIKE, THERE'S STILL A LOT OF THEM!

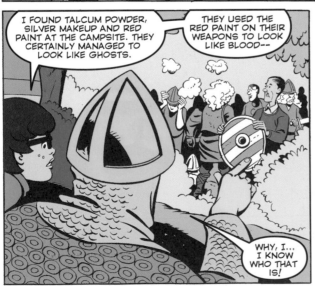

I FOUND TALCUM POWDER, SILVER MAKEUP AND RED PAINT AT THE CAMPSITE. THEY CERTAINLY MANAGED TO LOOK LIKE GHOSTS.

THEY USED THE RED PAINT ON THEIR WEAPONS TO LOOK LIKE BLOOD--

WHY, I... I KNOW WHO THAT IS!

LET'S SEE IF WE CAN SURPRISE THEM, SHALL WE?

SSSS

SUPER-SLEUTH WORDSEARCH!

Can you hunt down these missing words?
Tick them off as you find them.

S S P P L H L Z N M M W O U D S G N X
Q Z J J I L Y A F H L K F Q U E Z K M
Q A R S T A E V F K A F U I I Z O A A
A Y C R S E Y M O R Y S M J A D I L L
Y C S E E D F W Y A B Y K U M Z B N I T
C T Q E K I F W R I J H L A R X I K S S
Q M B I Y R U N U D N V R U K N J Z H
M I B Y I H X M L C S V U X V T I X O
B S S E Z Z R B L N U N C T V X W P
N I Z H M X Z B O L L U D N C U Z P H B J O
N W X B K C A N S Y B O O C S W N K U
N U Z F H W P D T Y Y C M N G Q D M P F Y
U F H O M L C H Z D L T B H Q M C J K D I G A R
I U S R E P E E J X N Y F S H O R H U R

Answers:

☐ Ruh Roh   ☐ Maltshop   ☐ Zoinks
☐ Jinkies   ☐ Coolsville   ☐ Jeepers
☐ Scooby Snack   ☐ Yikes

18

SCOOBY WHO?

Can you work who's hiding in these lines?
Colour all the shapes with a dot inside to find out!
Then tick the correct box

A

B

C

D

2. DYNAMITE BLAST

Light the dynamite by drawing a line from start to finish without touching the sides !

Well done, you got through the maze but the miner has blockd your path. You'll need to blast your way through with dynamite!

ROAD CLOSED!

START

FINISH

3. CODE CRACKER

Phew, YOU'RE THROUGH! Ok you've reached miner fortyniner's hidcout now to find Miner Fortyniner and that secret oil reserve, IT MUST BE BEHIND THS DOOR!

Q K G U F O S P
L O O D K Z C O
I I N K T S A Y

GOLD MINE
KEEP OUT

To find the door password, copy every third letter into the boxes below!

AW DAGNAB IT! THOSE MEDDLING KIDS!

NOT SO FAST, YOU TWO COWARDS!

NONE OF THE EYEWITNESS ACCOUNTS DESCRIBE THE SAME CREATURE.

WE'VE ALSO GOTTEN REPORTS *SIMULTANEOUSLY* FROM LOCATIONS THAT WERE *MILES APART!*

HERE'S ONE MORE FOR YOUR COLLECTION, CAPTAIN...

...LADY CLAIMS THAT SOME SORT OF *WITCH DOCTOR* WAS STEALING RUTABAGAS FROM HER VEGETABLE GARDEN!

WITCH DOCTOR?

RITCH ROCTOR?

I WONDER...

DON'T YOU WORRY, CAPTAIN MESSICK. WE'LL GET TO THE BOTTOM OF THIS MYSTERY.

I'D LIKE TO SEE A *MAP* SHOWING THE LOCATIONS OF THESE STRANGE OCCURRENCES, AND COPIES OF THE *POLICE REPORTS* AS WELL.

I'LL HAVE OFFICER NORTH HERE GET YOU EVERYTHING!

IF MY HUNCH IS CORRECT, THEN THIS MYSTERY SHOULD BE *EASY* TO SOLVE-- I HAVE A FEELING WE'VE DEALT WITH THIS WITCH DOCTOR *BEFORE.*

BUT *WHICH* WITCH DOCTOR? WE'VE DEALT WITH *TWO!*

THE INDIAN WITCH DOCTOR

REAL NAME: BUCK MASTERS
OCCUPATION: DOG TRAINER
LURKING LOCATION: INDIAN GAP
FIRST APPEARANCE: "DECOY FOR A DOGNAPPER"

THE MYSTERY, INC. GANG WAS CALLED TO A CASE INVOLVING *KIDNAPPED SHOW DOGS.* THE GANG DRESSED SCOOBY-DOO AS A CHAMPION GREAT DANE, IN HOPES THAT SCOOBY-DOO WOULD BE ABDUCTED. THE PLAN SUCCEEDED, AND A *TRACKING DEVICE* IN SCOOBY'S COLLAR LED THE GANG TO A DESERTED PUEBLO INDIAN VILLAGE. THERE, THEY FACED THE MYSTERIOUS *INDIAN WITCH DOCTOR*--WHO TURNED OUT TO BE BUCK MASTERS, A CHAMPION DOG BREEDER! MASTERS PLANNED TO WIN THE DOG SHOW BY KIDNAPPING THE COMPETITION!

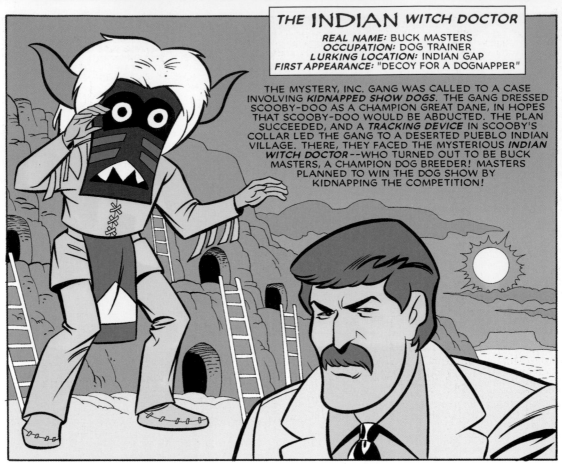

THE HAWAIIAN WITCH DOCTOR

REAL NAME: JOHN SIMMS
OCCUPATION: PEARL THIEF
LURKING LOCATION: ANCIENT HAWAIIAN VILLAGE
FIRST APPEARANCE: "A TIKI SCARE IS NO FAIR"

WHILE VACATIONING IN HAWAII, SCOOBY-DOO AND SHAGGY WERE WARNED BY THEIR HOST TO STAY AWAY FROM AN ANCIENT HAUNTED VILLAGE. SOON *GHOST DRUMS* BEGAN TO BEAT, AND A MYSTERIOUS WITCH DOCTOR APPEARED, WARNING EVERYONE THAT THE GOD *MANO TIKI TIA* WANTED THEM OFF THE FORBIDDEN GROUNDS AT ONCE. AS THE GOD HIMSELF APPEARED IN A GREAT CLOUD OF SMOKE, SCOOBY-DOO VANISHED!

FREDDIE, VELMA, AND DAPHNE PITCHED IN TO FIND SCOOBY-- AND BRAVED THE HAUNTED VILLAGE TO REVEAL MANO TIKI TIA AS NOTHING MORE THAN A HUGE *PARADE FLOAT!* THE HAWAIIAN WITCH DOCTOR WAS NONE OTHER THAN THEIR HOST, JOHN SIMMS, WHO SOUGHT TO FRIGHTEN OFF THE LOCAL FISHERMEN SO THAT HE COULD POACH THEIR *PEARLS!*

SO, LIKE, WHO LIVES HERE... ...THE ADDAMS FAMILY?

LIKE, I HOPE THE ART *INSIDE* IS FANTASTIC, 'CAUSE THE *OUTSIDE* COULDN'T PLEASE ANY ART CRITIC!

RATS REE RUTH!

WELL, THIS BUILDING'S BEEN *CLOSED* FOR YEARS. THE ART COLLECTION OUTGREW THE BUILDING.

THEY'RE STARTING TO MOVE IT INTO A BIGGER SPACE.

NO, SILLY-- THIS IS THE OLD *KASEM COUNTY MUSEUM OF ART.*

LIKE, I HOPE THE *NEW* PLACE IS MORE CHEERFUL...

CREEEEK

T-THAT'S FUNNY-- THE DOOR'S OPEN!

CAN I *HELP* YOU?

ZOINKS!

RIKES!

WH-WHO ARE *YOU?*

I'M FRANK WELKER. I *WORK* HERE.

THIS LATE? LIKE, WHO ARE YOU EXPECTING-- THE TOUR BUS FROM TRANSYLVANIA?

NO--I'M PREPARING THE CONTENTS OF THE MUSEUM FOR SHIPMENT TO THE *NEW SITE.* EACH ITEM MUST BE CAREFULLY PACKED, SO IT TAKES A LONG TIME.

NOW, WHO ARE *YOU*-- AND WHY ARE YOU HERE?

CONTINUED ON PAGE 32

MONSTER MASH-UP!

Zoinks! The gang have been turned into spooks, can you work out who each member of Mystery Inc. is?

A

B

C

D

E

Draw a line from each member of the gang to the correct monster!

1

2

3

4

5

Answers: A–5, B–4, C–1, D–3, E–2.

29

MEMORY MASH!

Look at this freaky scene for one minute, then cover it up and answer the questions on the right hand page!

FINALLY. MY FEET ARE KILLING ME!

THERE'S A POLICE CAR HERE. I WONDER WHAT'S GOING ON?

CAPTAIN MESSICK!

I'M GLAD TO SEE THE TWO OF YOU.

YOU CAN FORGET ABOUT YOUR WITCH DOCTOR. THIS TIME WE'VE GOT BETTER EVIDENCE THAN AN EYEWITNESS DESCRIPTION!

THIS CREATURE JUST HELD UP THIS GAS STATION, AND THEY GOT HIM ON TAPE...

THE WEREWOLF! I REMEMBER HIM!

YOU DO?

THAT'S ODD. THIS CRIME SEEMS SO PETTY AND SIMPLE, COMPARED TO THE ELABORATE SCHEME HE WAS UP TO WHEN WE FIRST ENCOUNTERED HIM.

THERE'S SOMETHING ELSE ODD ABOUT THAT VIDEO...

I'LL MAKE SOME CALLS. IN THE MEANTIME, ANY CHANCE YOU COULD GIVE OUR VAN A TOW? IT'S OUT BY THE OLD ART MUSEUM WITH A FLAT.

YOU BET. WILL IT BE EASY TO RECOGNIZE?

REMEMBER HOW SHAGGY AND SCOOBY SHAVED THE HAIR OFF THAT WEREWOLF? HE SHOULD BE BALD!

Hmm. JERRY, THE ATTENDANT ON DUTY, SAID THE WEREWOLF LOOKED LIKE HE WAS WEARING A TOUPEÉ. MAYBE HE WAS?

Oh, IT SURE WILL!

THE **WEREWOLF**

REAL NAME: SILAS LONG
OCCUPATION: SHEEP RUSTLER
LURKING LOCATION: CREEPY CAMPSITE
FIRST APPEARANCE: "WHO'S AFRAID OF THE BIG BAD WEREWOLF?"

WHEN THE MYSTERY INC. GANG WENT CAMPING, STRANGE GROWLING SOUNDS LED THEM TO A TRAIL OF *WOLF FOOTPRINTS*--FOOTPRINTS THAT BELONGED TO A WOLF WHO WALKS ON *TWO LEGS!* THEY LED IN TURN TO THE OPENED GRAVE OF *SILAS LONG*--A MAN WHO WAS HALF-MAN AND HALF-WOLF, AND WHO NOW APPARENTLY WALKS AGAIN!

BRAVING BOOBY-TRAPPED BOATHOUSES, BARRELS FITTED WITH BREATHING TUBES, AND OTHER MYSTERIOUS PROPS, THE GANG UNCOVERED A SHEEP RUSTLER'S PLOT OF STEALING SHEEP AND FLOATING THEM DOWNSTREAM IN THE RIGGED BARRELS, TO BE RETRIEVED BY AN ACCOMPLICE!

HERE LIES
_ _AS LONG
HALF-MAN
AND
HALF-WOLF

THE GIGGLING GREEN **GHOST**

REAL NAME: COSGOOD CREEPS
OCCUPATION: LAWYER
LURKING LOCATION: HAUNTED MANSION
FIRST APPEARANCE: "A NIGHT OF FRIGHT IS NO DELIGHT"

AN ECCENTRIC MILLIONAIRE COLONEL LEFT *ONE MILLION DOLLARS* TO FOUR RELATIVES AND--SCOOBY-DOO, WHO ONCE RESCUED HIM FROM A FISH POND!

COSGOOD CREEPS, THE ATTORNEY OF THE LATE COLONEL, THEN REVEALED THAT SCOOBY-DOO HAD TO SPEND THE *WHOLE NIGHT* IN THE HAUNTED MANSION TO GET THE MONEY! THE GANG STUCK AROUND AND WOUND UP DEALING WITH *GROWLING FISH, TRAP DOORS, SPOOKY WRITTEN CLUES,* AND A PAIR OF *GIGGLING GREEN GHOSTS!*

TRACES OF GREEN PAINT FROM THE "GHOSTS" LED THE GANG TO SET AN ELABORATE TRAP, REVEALING THE GHOSTS TO BE MR. CREEPS AND HIS PARTNER MR. CRAWLS, WHO PLANNED TO SCARE EVERYONE OFF THE ISLAND AND GRAB THE FORTUNE. UNFORTUNATELY, THAT FORTUNE TURNED OUT TO BE *WORTHLESS CIVIL WAR MONEY!*

CONTINUED ON PAGE 40

CREEPY COLOUR

GRAB YOUR COLOURING PENS AND GO COLOUR CRAZY ON THIS SCARY SCENE!

THE TELESCOPE GHOST

REAL NAME: "BLUESTONE THE GREAT"
OCCUPATION: STAGE MAGICIAN/
TREASURE HUNTER
LURKING LOCATION:
VASQUEZ CASTLE ON HAUNTED ISLE
FIRST APPEARANCE: "HASSLE IN
THE CASTLE"

ON A BOATING TRIP, SCOOBY AND THE GANG RAN AGROUND IN THE FOG AND FOUND THEMSELVES ON SPOOKY HAUNTED ISLE, HOME OF *VASQUEZ CASTLE*. THE 17th-CENTURY PIRATE VASQUEZ ALLEGEDLY HID A TREASURE SOMEWHERE IN THE CASTLE!

THE GANG ENCOUNTERED A *TALKING SKULL*, A *HAM SANDWICH* APPEARING OUT OF THIN AIR, A *FLYING CARPET*--AND EVENTUALLY DISCOVERED THAT MAGIC TRICKS WERE RESPONSIBLE FOR ALL OF THEM, EXCEPT FOR THE GHOST WHO FLOATED THROUGH WALLS. WHEN THE GHOST WAS REVEALED TO BE THE EX-MAGICIAN "BLUESTONE THE GREAT," HE REVEALED HE DID IT WITH *MIRRORS*!

THE MAN FROM MARS

REAL NAME: CHARLIE THE FUNLAND ROBOT
OCCUPATION: AMUSEMENT PARK OPERATOR
LURKING LOCATION: FUNLAND AMUSEMENT PARK
FIRST APPEARANCE: "FOUL PLAY IN FUNLAND"

WHILE CLAM-DIGGING NEXT TO A DESERTED AMUSEMENT PARK, SCOOBY AND THE GANG NOTICED RIDES OPERATING WITH NO PASSENGERS. WHEN THEY QUESTIONED THE PARK'S CARETAKER, HE DENIED ANY STRANGE HAPPENINGS. THE GANG THEN SPOTTED A FREAKY-LOOKING CREATURE ATOP THE FERRIS WHEEL THAT WAS SETTING RIDES INTO MOTION!

AFTER CHASING IT AROUND THE FAIRWAY, THE ROLLER COASTER AND THE TUNNEL OF LOVE, THEY DISCOVERED IT WAS A *ROBOT!* THE CARETAKER CONFESSED TO CREATING IT TO RUN THE PARK--AND THE CARETAKER'S *WIFE* CONFESSED TO RIGGING IT TO RUN HAYWIRE, BECAUSE SHE DIDN'T WANT IT AROUND CHILDREN!

CAPTAIN CUTLER'S GHOST

REAL NAME: CAPTAIN CUTLER
OCCUPATION: SEA CAPTAIN/BOAT THIEF
LURKING LOCATION: THE GRAVEYARD OF SHIPS
FIRST APPEARANCE: "A CLUE FOR SCOOBY-DOO"

WHILE SURFING AT A BEACH PARTY, SCOOBY-DOO ENCOUNTERED THE GLOWING GHOST OF A SEA CAPTAIN. THE GANG ALSO LEARNED THAT YACHTS WERE DISAPPEARING IN THE AREA, AND THAT THE DISAPPEARANCES WERE BLAMED ON *CAPTAIN CUTLER'S GHOST!*

WEARING SCUBA GEAR, THE KIDS SEARCHED THE WRECKAGE OF DOZENS OF SUNKEN SHIPS IN "THE GRAVEYARD OF SHIPS." HERE, THEY DISCOVERED A SEA CAVE FILLED WITH THE MISSING BOATS-- INTACT AND REPAINTED!

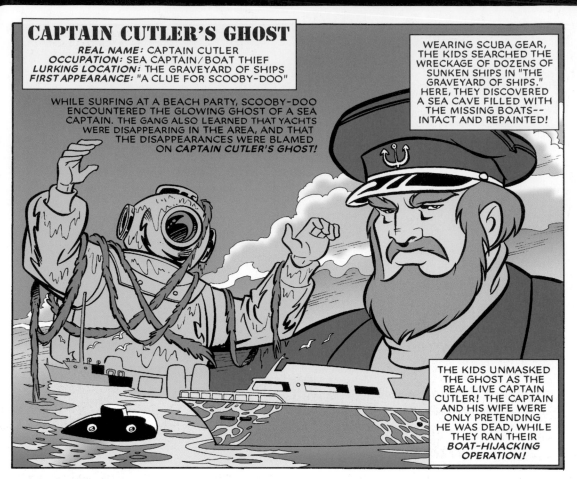

THE KIDS UNMASKED THE GHOST AS THE REAL LIVE CAPTAIN CUTLER! THE CAPTAIN AND HIS WIFE WERE ONLY PRETENDING HE WAS DEAD, WHILE THEY RAN THEIR *BOAT-HIJACKING OPERATION!*

THE SPACE KOOK

REAL NAME: HENRY BASCOMB
OCCUPATION: SCHEMING REAL ESTATE CROOK
LURKING LOCATION: ABANDONED AIRFIELD
FIRST APPEARANCE: "SPOOKY SPACE KOOK"

THE MYSTERY MACHINE RAN OUT OF GAS, AND THE GANG WENT TO AN OLD FARMHOUSE LOOKING FOR HELP. THE FARMER GREETED THEM COLDLY, MISTAKING THEM FOR SNOOPY REPORTERS. NEWSPEOPLE HADN'T LEFT HIM ALONE EVER SINCE AN EERIE CRAFT WAS SEEN HOVERING OVER HIS FIELDS AT NIGHT!

THE GANG FOLLOWED *GLOWING FOOTPRINTS* TO AN OLD ABANDONED AIRFIELD--ONLY TO CONFRONT A SPOOKY ASTRONAUT WITH A SKULL FOR A FACE! USING A WIND TUNNEL AS A TRAP, THEY FOUND THE SPACE KOOK TO BE A SCHEMER TRYING TO SCARE THE FARMER INTO SELLING HIS LAND CHEAP--SO HE COULD TURN AROUND AND SELL THE OLD AIRFIELD TO THE AIR FORCE!

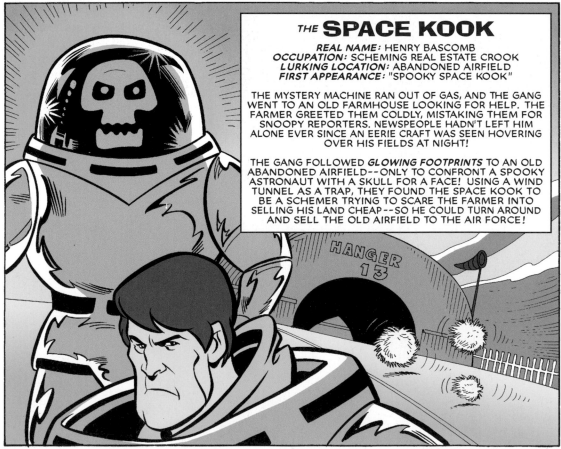

HAUNTED HOLDER!

FOLLOW THESE EASY STEPS TO CREATE YOUR OWN HAUNTED HOUSE DESK TIDY! ZOINKS, IT'S LIKE, TOTALLY SPOOKTASTIC!

1 Cut the top off your cardboard box. Trim the front so that it is about 8cm high, and trim the sides so that they slope down to meet the front of the box.

2 Cut a piece of thick card the same width as the box and about 12cm high. Slot it into the centre of the box, and fix in place with sticky tape.

48

YOU WILL NEED:

A CARDBOARD BOX - THICK CARD - NEWSPAPERS - PVA GLUE -
PAINTS AND PAINTBRUSH - STICKY TAPE - CARDBOARD TUBE

3 Draw the shape of a haunted house on a piece of cardboard. Now draw two ghosts, two bats and two tombstones. Cut each of the shapes out.

4 Trim the back section of the box into a wavy line and stick the haunted house in the centre. Glue the ghosts and tombstone to the middle section and the two bats to the front. Now cover the whole box in a layer of PVA glue and torn-up newspaper and leave it to dry.

5 Tape a cardboard tube inside the back section as this will make a stand for your pencils. Now you can paint your stationery holder in creepy colours! Check it out, you're ready to store your stationery with spooky style!

I TOLD LAURA DAD'S JUST *CRACKING UP!*

≷SIGH≶ THIS IS MY BROTHER LUKE. PLEASE EXCUSE HIM -- SOMETIMES HE CAN BE *SO* CRASS!

THEY SAY THE *CRASS* IS ALWAYS *CREENER* ON THE OTHER SIDE!

RHEE, HEE, HEE!

YES! THE *OTHER SIDE!* I BELIEVE THERE'S SOME-THING *PARANORMAL* GOING ON IN THIS HOUSE!

SO, THE FAMILY COMPANY IS CALLED *HUGHES INDUSTRIES.* WHAT DOES IT MANUFACTURE?

WE HAVE A LOT OF GOVERNMENT CONTRACTS FOR DIFFERENT PROJECTS.

BUT WE SPECIALISE IN *ULTRA-MINIATURISATION!*

THIS WRISTWATCH IS ACTUALLY A *DIGITAL CAMERA* CAPABLE OF PRODUCING A PHOTO WITH *7.1 MILLION PIXELS!*

MAYBE THEY COULD MINIATURISE OUR *STOMACHS!* THEN WE WOULDN'T BE SO *HUNGRY* ALL THE TIME, EH, SCOOB?

RUNH-UH! RI RIKE RUNGER!

WELL, GOTTA RUN. NICE MEETING YOU ALL!

AND THIS IS A COMPUTER AS *POWERFUL* AS THE *FASTEST DESKTOP*, YET *BARELY* THE SIZE OF A *CREDIT CARD!*

JINKIES! THEY'LL HAVE TO *MINIATURISE* YOUR *FINGERS* SO YOU CAN *TYPE* ON IT!

YOU *DON'T* TYPE ON IT! IT'S TOTALLY *VOICE-CONTROLLED!*

LIKE, I HAD AN IDEA FOR AN INVENTION!

I WAS WORKING ON *"FREEZE-DRIED WATER,"* BUT IT KEEPS *MELTING!*

REAH! ROO ROLD! BRRRR!

HELP! HELP!

DADDY!

YOU'RE SAFE, SIR! THERE'S NOBODY HERE!

PLEASE, MELISSA! PLEASE!

OH, NO, SIR, YOU'RE MISTAKEN! I'M VELMA AND SHE'S DAPHNE!

MELISSA IS MY *MOTHER'S* NAME. HE'S HEARING HER *VOICE* AGAIN!

CONTINUED ON PAGE 56

GHOULISH GALLERY!

Can you find the 10 creepy changes we've made to this freaky scene?

Tick each time you spot a change! ☐ ☐ ☐ ☐ ☐ ☐ ☐ ☐ ☐ ☐

COULD THIS BE THE ENTRANCE TO A *COOKIE MINE?* OR MAYBE, LIKE, A *SCOOBY SNACK SHACK?*

RUMMY!

PICK UP ANY SWEET SCENTS?

RILREW!

MILDEW, HUH? WHAT *FLAVOR?* HA, HA, HA!

!

THAT LOOKS LIKE MY MOTHER!

WELL, THIS TIME *I* SEE IT!

BUT I *STILL* DON'T *HEAR* HER!

NOOOOO!!

OH, YOU'RE *HEARING* THINGS, ALL RIGHT!

BUT IT'S WHATEVER SOMEONE *WANTS* YOU TO HEAR!

AND HERE COMES THAT *SOMEONE* NOW!

LUKE, STOP PUSHING ME!

MOTHER, *I'M* NOT PUSHING *YOU*... SOMEONE'S PUSHING *ME*!

LUKE, *WHAT* IS THIS ALL ABOUT?

MELISSA, WHAT WERE YOU DOING DOWN IN THE CATACOMBS?

TRYING TO DRIVE *YOU* INSANE-- BY TRANSMITTING HER VOICE THROUGH THAT *EAR GADGET*!

I'VE BEEN TRYING TO GET YOU TO RETIRE AND LET *LUKE* TAKE OVER THE COMPANY FOR *YEARS*, YOU OLD *FOOL*!

AND IT WOULD HAVE WORKED THIS TIME, EVEN IF I HAD TO HAVE YOU DECLARED *INCOMPETENT*!

BUT, LIKE, I DON'T GET IT! WHY DID THEY JUST *COME OUT* WHEN THEIR PLAN WAS WORKING SO WELL?

WHEN WE MADE YOU LEAVE, WE SENT RALPH-- IN THE CHAMELEON SUIT-- AFTER YOU!

Velma's Detective Test!

Good detectives are always paying attention super sleuths! Were you paying attention during the the comic strips in this annual?

1 Yikes! It's The Vikings!
What was Velma really holding?

A

B

C

2 Who's Who in Scooby-Doo
Here's the Indian Witch Doctor, can you spot something we've changed about him?

3 Take a close look at this scene. Can you spot 5 things that look out of place.

4 Hear No Evil
Who are these two shadowy characters?

Shaggy

Scooby

Velma

Fred

Daphne

5 Can you spot 5 things in this scene that don't belong there.

Answers: 1) B. 2) The Witch Doctor has pink hair now. 3) The Ghost is wearing a witches hat, An Alien in the clock. Velma is wearing a pink jumper, The Ghost is wearing glasses, pots and pans on the wall. 4) Daphne and Velma. 5) Hanging Spider, TV on shelves, Huge Sea Monster, No Dogs Allowed sign, Daphne is wearing red.

MINI MYSTERY ??

The fingerprints are on pages: 10, 12, 19, 20, 27, 39, 45, 52, 61, 63,

61